CHANNEL >>ZERO

written, illustrated, designed by
Brian Wood

editorial assistance by Michelle Lo

LA DEMOCRATIE

disinfect

the path we tread...

1. Шйптʼч тйе плот чммару оф Сйаннел ишро?

The first part of Channel Zero, the four-issue miniseries, is set in NYC, right now. Broadcast media and print media have been taken over by the government, giving them control over content. This came in the form of the Clean Act *(Фтйдж Кийа)*, a bill that was forced through Congress and signed into law under pressure from special interest groups, most notably the Christian Right *(Дие то АЛК йфу)* and Pro-Censorship Parents groups. Most of the populace went along with the change, either in support of the change, or too lazy to do anything about it. This demonstates the dangers of apathy.

2. Шйътʼч тйе протагонинтʼч обжестиве...шйч?

The protagonist is Jennie 2.5, an ex-performance artist made obsolete by the Clean Act, who cannot understand or accept the fact that her friends and peers just sit by while the government censors their lives. With a little help from a tiny struggling anti-government *(гдчги йкж йъвоп жк)* underground resistance, she comes up with a plan to broadcast a pirate televison show, public-access style, in hopes of reaching people brainwashed by the propaganda thats around them, and convince them they need to take action, regain control of their lives. Her motives cannot be so pure, however, and a certain amount of ego and her desire to be famous comes very close to overpowering her "moral desire to do whats right."

...

ПОКАЈАЊЕ

Дела 3:19

Покајте се дакле, и обратите се да се очистите од гријеха својијех, да дођу времена одмарања од лица Господњега.

Лука 13:3

Не, кажем вам; него ако се не покајете, сви ћете тако изгинути.

Матеј 3:2

И говораше: покајте се, јер се приближи царство небеско.

II Коринћанима 7:10

Јер жалост која је по Богу доноси за спасеније покајање, за које се нигда не каје; а жалост овога свијета смрт доноси.

БЛАГОДАТ ИСУСА ХРИСТА

Римљанима 5:15

Али дар није тако као гријех; јер кад кроз гријех једнога помријеше многи, много се већма благодат Божија и дар изли изобилно на многе благодаћу једнога човјека Исуса Христа.

II Коринћанима 9:15

А хвала Богу на његову неисказаноме дару.

Римљанима 9:16

Тако дакле нити стоји до онога који хоће, ни до онога који трци, него до Бога који помилује.

II Коринћанима 8:9

Јер знате благодат Господа нашега Исуса Христа да, богат будући, вас ради осиромаши, да се ви његовијем сиромаштвом обогатите.

YOUR MIND IS A WEAPON.
USE IT.

Date: Fri, 29 Jan 1999 19:49:36 -0500
From: WARREN ELLIS <WarrenEllis@compuserve.com>
Subject: Happy Birthday
Sender: WARREN ELLIS <WarrenEllis@compuserve.com>
To: brianwood <channelbri@bigfoot.com>
MIME-Version: 1.0
Status: O

Happy birthday, mate.

Is the following good enough? I can alter and
expand it during tomorrow, if you'd like, no
problem.

Cheers,

warren

****

CHANNEL ZERO

Pop culture rolled over and died some time ago. Some
people actually think Marilyn Manson is scary, that Kurt
Cobain had something to do with rebellion, that Bret
Easton Ellis is a dangerous writer, that it's a good thing
that you can buy McDonalds in Prague, that movies are
somehow relevant to our lives.

Television is our stage and our anaesthetic. Real life
happens on television in preference to
our homes and streets. People resolve their relationships
on freakshow chatshows instead of in living rooms
or beds or even goddamn bars.

And it spreads. Rupert Murdoch beams his shit into
Asia, English children are taught that Z is pronounced
Zee by goddamn Barney, and all of a sudden world
cultures become the Monoculture, the same conversation,
the same clothes, the same show. All tuned to
Channel Zero.

And, all over the world, one by one, we quit fighting it.
we sit and we put the book we're reading down and
laugh at the arseholes on Jerry Springer, snigger
at Matthew Perry, get our news managed for us
by CNN, and suddenly we're like all the rest. We're
in cultural lockstep, taking holidays in other people's
misery, asking for our stinking badges, dead heads
nodding over phosphordot fixes.

Someone's remembered what comics are for.

In goddamn America, of all places.

Meet Brian Wood.

Over here in comics, things are different, you see. Sometimes we're an outlaw medium. Sometimes we're just the preferred tiny place for neurotics and losers to gibber in. Either way, we're an outside art, a fringe medium watched by no-one but the more voracious cultural commentators and the aficionados. We don't have huge corporations trembling at our every movement, because we make no money compared to the other visual narrative media. That vast commercial pressure isn't brought to bear on comics. Which means, often, that we can say what we want without rich men's scissors attacking our work until it's safe for little Tommy in Dogshit, Nebraska. I hate little Tommy in Dogshit, Nebraska. I want to kill little Tommy in Dogshit, Nebraska. And so does Brian Wood.

Brian Wood remembers how to be angry. He remembers how to wake up in the morning and look out at this plastic MTV-soundtracked world we've agreed to exist in and get pissed off with it. And he goes to his desk and makes buzzing, scratchy, shuddering people, the innards of the people-shaped things he sees lockstepping down the street outside, and he puts them in a crazed, broken America that really is just the America we know seen through a cleaner window, and he makes those people move the way they should. He makes them talk about revolution. He makes them spark and snarl and scheme and scream the way pop culture icons are supposed to. They rant and rail against the dying of the light the way people should.

The longer CHANNEL ZERO runs, the purer it becomes. It grows dominated by symbols, huge dark images of a beaten world filled with a beaten generation, the place that, like Ginsberg howled, saw its best minds destroyed. Black things grow out of the pages, looming over and burying Jennie 2.5 and Channel Zero's other hopeful monsters. The semiotics of a heartdead world hit like gunfire -- but, in the interstices, you begin to hear music. Anger and passion rise up again. For all its black and white somber mien, CHANNEL ZERO is, to me, one of the most uplifting comics of the Nineties. CHANNEL ZERO is about winning. It's about learning how to give a shit again, about finding ways to make things better. It's about anger as a positive force of creation. It's about your right to not have to live in the world they've built for you.

It's about turning off the television.

-- Warren Ellis

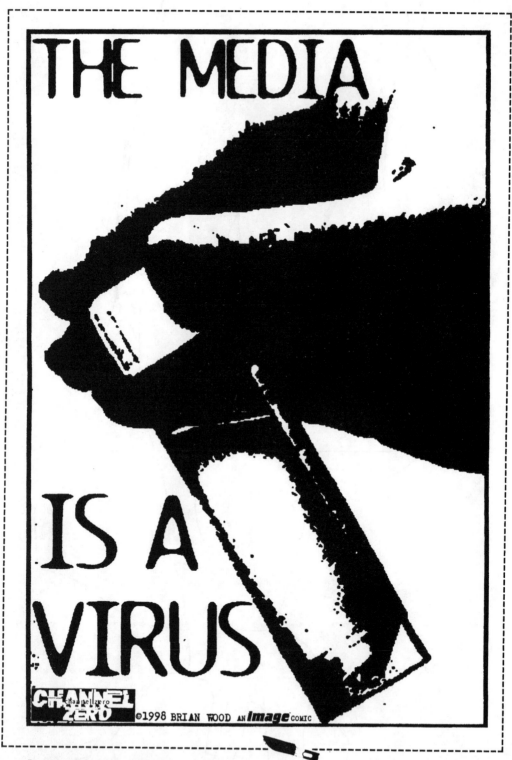

THE MEDIA
IS A VIRUS

CHANNEL ZERO ©1998 BRIAN WOOD AN *Image* COMIC

photocopy this page!

your basic rights are under assault. don't
wait for others to do it for you. use the
power you have and fight back. help spread
the word.   your future is yours.

YOUR MIND IS A WEAPON.
USE IT.

DAT

CLEAN

consumer

6194 2 448 2

WORSHIP

HYPER ARMA

TRUTH

LIMIT

BE GENTLE

The M Network

URACHADH

CHOICE

ALBANNAICH

.taste the tangible.

GLOBAL

DRTY

DANCE

5

ork was different back then,
hen I was a student. Hell, the
country was different. I was
ng the pavement looking for
arrogant as fuck with my
e in Media and Popular
ence, completely missing the
ng signs.

hristian Right were all up in
M.A.N.I. was everywhere, pick-
networks, bookstores, you name
Even creepy-assed Parents for
l Responsibility was into it,
he result of this unholy unity
he Clean Act. For awhile I was
d off at the government for pass-
hat law, but now I can see they
t have a choice. They were com-
ly out-gunned, and I have a
ng if they had resisted, there
d have been a revolution, and
ultra-paranoid christian
emist parents running the coun-
we would REALLY be fucked.

ONLY WAY

"So the government took control of the media, and I saw my future career disappear before it even started. What use was there for a hard-core, truth-seeking, idealist freelance journalist like me in a country where the news is filtered, edited, packaged and sanitized for our protection?

"I took a bullshit staff job, monitoring worldwide wire feeds, sifting out the 'unfit to print' news and passing along the ones I knew my censor would allow. And I wrote. I wrote and wrote and documented and catalogued and observed. I knew that eventually the country would get back to normal, and I would have a complete record of the whole fucking unpleasant experience.

"And it would be worth a fortune.

"As is usually the case, even in a city under lockdown, an underground culture exists and thrives, an illegal alternative "scene", formed in retaliation to whatever or whomever is in control. Nothing too powerful, though. Most of the country doesn't give a shit about what was happening.

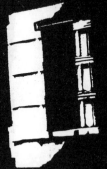

REZ ZURЯECTION

SHUT UP

"They have their TV and newspapers, filled with positive reassurances and government propaganda that always seems to make everyone feel better about themselves. The ten o'clock news is full of celebrity gossip, stories about puppies being rescued from burning buildings, and reviews of the newest Disney film.

"And people seem to like that just fine.

trust yourself

**REZ
RRECTION**

"Most people anyway. The ones who don't
lack the drive to do anything about it.

doot sell what you have not

9 788980 515288

ISBN 89-SINNER-8-6
ISBN 89-8051-527-8

"During this time, a kind of bizarre
club scene was flourishing in certain
areas of the Lower East Side.

"I was never into the club
scene, even back before.
I prefer a dark beer in an
even darker bar. These new
places are more like fucked-
up social clubs for the self-
proclaimed elite. They support a tech black-market,
where you can score illegal
software, like content fil-
ters, firewall crack codes,
foreign access chips.

HR 67 10   DDE 82 24   UYE

HAS JUST

"People hang out, brag
a lot, drink 'smart
drinks', and watch
bootlegged European
broadcasting.

Generation Tech (GenTech): a youth subculture on the rise, characterized by a technology fetish and a lessened desire for human contact.

trust your technolust

ZURRECTION

damn nation

"I've never spent any great amount of time in any of these places, and the picture the news paints of them is pretty negative, but it doesn't matter.

"Inside one of these uber-geek hangouts, surrounded by greed and way too much fucking attitude, this is where it started.

YOU ARE HERE

LIMIT

CLEAN

DIRTY

REPENT

DAT

"A new America.

america is waiting for a message of one sort or another

"And I can't think of a more appropriate place."

STUDENT FILM PROJECT.

the truth is a concept

STUDENT FILM PROJECT. *RIGHT.* YOU ARE THAT WIERDO *PERFORMANCE ARTIST* CHICK, RIGHT? I SAW YOU A WHILE BACK. YOU *SUCK.* YOU HAVE THE *MONEY* FOR THIS *SHIT?*

WAKE UP

YEAH, WHENEVER AND WHEREVER. LOOK, LETS GET OUT OF HERE, OK?

YOU HEAR HOW THEY BUSTED THAT PUBLIC ACCESS CABLE COOPERATIVE A COUPLE DAYS AGO?

YEAH, SO WHAT? SHIT LIKE THAT HAPPENS..... OH WAIT *OH SHIT*. DONT *TELL ME* YOU WANT THIS STUFF FOR *BROADCAST.* NO WAY, ITS IMPOSSIBLE. EVEN WITH THE HARDWARE, YOU *STILL* NEED TELCO CODES, AND *THAT* SHIT IS ENCRYPTED, NOT TO MENTION BEHIND FIREWALLS LIKE YOU WOULD *NOT* BELIEVE.

I DIDN'T ASK YOU FOR ANY *CODES.* ALL I NEED FROM *YOU* IS WHAT'S ON MY *LIST.*

WITHOUT THE *BROADCAST CODES*, ALL YOU CAN DO WITH THAT HARDWARE IS MAKE *FANCY HOME MOVIES*. YOU CANT BRING *SHIT* LIKE THIS OUT IN THE OPEN. THERE ARE MANDATORY JAIL TERMS FOR EVEN *POSSESSING* HIGH END VIDEO EQUIPMENT WITHOUT LICENSE.

I CAN HANDLE IT.

YOU CAN HANDLE IT. SHIT, *GOOD FOR YOU.*

its a feeling!

LOOK. WHEN THEY CLOSED DOWN THAT CABLE COOPERATIVE, THEY CLOSED DOWN THE *LAST PRIVATE-OPERATED OUTLET OF EXPRESSION.* ITS COMPLETE, ITS *FINISHED.* THE COUNTRY IS *TOTALLY CENSORED!* DON'T YOU *GIVE A SHIT?*

NOT REALLY. I'M DOING ALRIGHT. WHO CARES? ANYWAY, WHAT CAN I DO?

WHAT YOU CAN *DO* IS FILL MY ORDER BY DAY AFTER TOMORROW. AND GO BACK TO PEDDLING PORN FILMS AND CHEAP JAPANESE ELECTRONICS. AND SHUT THE *FUCK* UP. YOU NEVER SAW ME.

POINT AND SHOOT

w h e n   y o u   s p e a k ,   t h e   s o u n d   o f   y o u r   v o i c e   c a n c e l s   o u t   a l l   o t h e r s

шйо шатсйеч шйо? шйо шатсйеч шйо? шйо шатсйеч уоъ?

With th e advent of the affordable **portable** video camera, multiple   watch groups and activist sects have sprung up worldwide, operating in such hot spots as *****Eastern Europe**, the former **Soviet Union**,   N orthern Ireland, and urban areas **across the** United States.

i r r i t a i n m e n t

villinokivic--

monday, dec 12.

4 students were killed yesterday in the latest clash between the USF and state police. the confrontation erupted when the police attempted to deter the students from publically airing amateur video footage of alleged human rights abuses by the police during last months demonstrations.

w h o   w a t c h e s   w h o ?   w h o   w a t c h e s   y o u ?

..clashes between British troops and pro-independence terrorists agan claimed the lives of several tourists. while such incidents are be~oming commonplace, eyewitnesses say the tourists were specifically targeted by the troops because they were filming the demonstration. the families of the victims are outraged, and at this time, Scotland Yard has declined to comment. a search has uncovered   no   video   cameras   or   video   cassettes   in   the   vicinity...

YOUR MIND IS A WEAPON. USE IT.

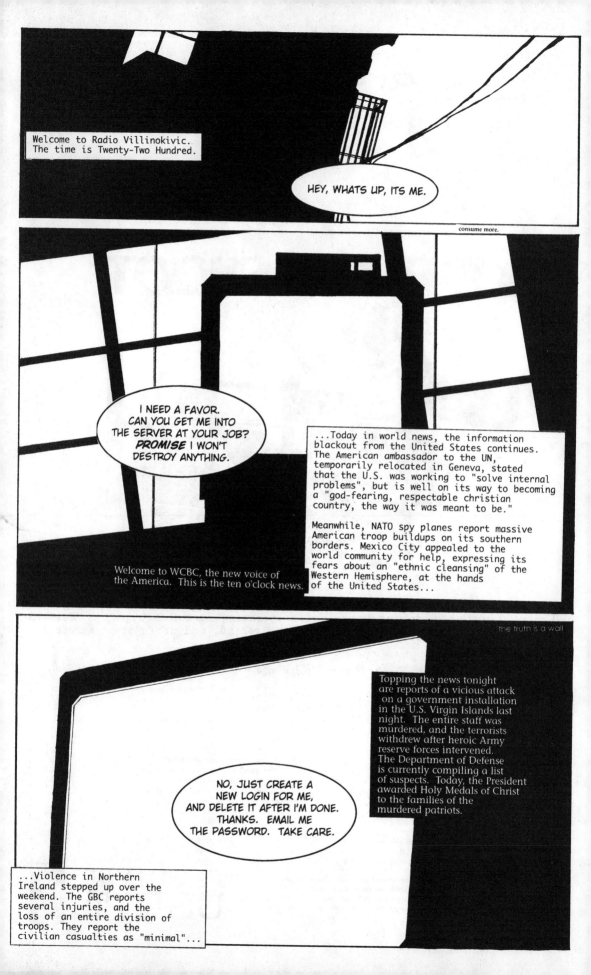

SUCKERS.

NO, NOT YOU, HOLD ON, LET ME PUT YOU ON *SPEAKER*. OK, GIVE IT TO ME.

I'M MODEMING YOU A NUMBER AND LOGIN INFO FOR A SMALL-TIME *ISP* IN *BELGRADE*. GO IN THROUGH THERE AND CREATE A HOTMAIL ACCOUNT AND COME *BACK* THROUGH THAT. GOT IT?

In local news, the Mayor of New York approved a measure to allow troops to be stationed in Ellis Island. The move is not so much anti-immigrant, the Mayor said, as it is pro-Democracy, pro-Christian, and pro-American.

JUST ABOUT. THEN WHAT?

On Wall Street, demonstrators protesting American financial backing of what they call "death squads" were arrested en masse and transported to Rikers Island for processing. The incorrect slanderous term used by the protesters is in reference to recent missionary activities in South America.

PICK ANY *BBS* OFF THE LIST I EMAILED YOU LAST NIGHT, AND ENTER "TEST" AS BOTH *LOGIN* AND *PASSWORD*. I SET UP ROOT ACCOUNTS FOR ALL OF THEM. FROM THERE, YOU ARE *FREE AND CLEAR*. ARE YOU ON A *T1* LINE?

...Denying claims that the recent reunification of the former Soviet states means a return to closed-borders rule, St. Petersburg issues what they call "free citizen passes", plastic swipe cards that guarantee freedom of passage to all citizens of New BelaRussia...

YEAH, I'M SIGNED ON THROUGH THE SERVERS AT STATICOM.

COOL, LET ME KNOW HOW IT GOES.

A recent poll indicated that 80% of Americans that expressed an opinion believe that the President should be allowed to seek a third term in office. The remaining 20% of participating citizens didn't.

OK, I WILL. THANKS.

New BelaRussia, the communist confederation formed by the reunification of the former Soviet States, has closed its borders and returned to its Cold War era status as an enemy of America, and all god-fearing individuals everywhere.

South Africa took an unexpected step into the world media arena with the debut of Radio Free Africa, a public access forum designed to give citizens the right to "speak freely", stating that such a right is "hard to come by, but necessary" in today's society.

buy american!

HEY, ITS ME AGAIN. TURN ON THE WCBC NEWS. OF *COURSE* ITS *SHIT*, BUT TURN IT ON ANYWAY AND JUST *WAIT*. I'M TRYING SOMETHING.

ARE YOU HACKING WCBC?

SO WHAT IF I AM.

...Havana today announced its decision to discontinue its "open-door" policy of allowing immigrants from the U.S. into Cuba. Describing a severe shortage of resources, government officials described the new policy as "regrettable"...

SHIT, I DIDNT KNOW *THAT*. *GET OUT OF THERE*. THE CODES AND ACCOUNTS I CREATED FOR YOU *WON'T WORK*. THE SECURITY THERE WILL *BURN* YOU.

trust me

DONT WORRY, I *KNOW* WHAT I'M DOING.

IM SERIOUS! THEY *AUTOMATICALLY* BACK-TRACE *ALL* INCOMING CALLS. THEY WILL HAVE YOU IN *LESS THAN A MINUTE.*

THAT WOULD BE TRUE, BUT I'M NOT *ON* A CONVENTIONAL PHONE LINE.

WHAT ARE YOU ON?

NO SHIT? FOR REAL? WHERE DID YOU GET THE *HARDWARE?* CERTAINLY NOT FROM *ME.*

FBI agents raided and confiscated the contents of a suspected child pornographer's apartment today. Neighbors reported the pervert to local police, who, after searching the garbage outside the apartment complex, determined there was sufficent reason for the raid.

I HAVE A *DISH* ON MY ROOF. I'M *LINKED DIRECT* TO THEIR SATELLITE. I'M GOING ON THE *AIR.*

I GOT A FEW SOURCES. IT WASN'T *CHEAP*, BUT IT WILL BE WORTH IT. NOW GO WATCH TV. I'M JUST ABOUT *READY.*

...Terrorists again attempted a takeover of a fiber-optic telecommunications substation located on the U.S. Virgin Islands. The attempted takeover was unsuccessful.

The substation is responsible for relaying information from North America to Africa and parts of Europe. A coded message from a terrorist cell located in New York claimed responsibility for the attack, saying that possessing the substation is "key" in order to maintain "unpolluted world dialogue"...

dont be a puppet

A new televison rating system proposed by the Vice-President goes into effect March 1st. It will help parents customize their programming choices for their children. The new system is hailed by parents groups across the country.

"My mother used to tell me how she could always remember where she was when JFK was killed. She remembered where she was when the Iranian hostages were released. She even remembers watching the news when Reagan was shot.

"I don't remember where I was when the Berlin Wall came down, when the cold war "officially" ended, or when the Gulf War started. But sure as shit, clear as day, I remember this.

"Something really stupid was on TV that night. Then it happened. The picture went all static, and before I could curse out the cable company, these images started flashing on the screen."

2.5

COOL.

"It was literally out of nowhere. Television had turned our brains to shit with its Top 100 Video Countdowns and reruns of Seinfeld. But when I saw those 3 seconds of broadcast, I knew something big was about to happen."

Welcome to Radio Villinokivic. The time is Oh-Six Hundred. Good Morning.

Watch groups in Berlin last night reported what appeared to be 4 seconds of illegal broadcast on WCBC television. Normal programming was interrupted by a series of images and phrases. The source of the broadcast is unknown, although experts believe it was an electronic break-in originating on American soil.

Strangely, there has been no report of this incident on any American news sources.

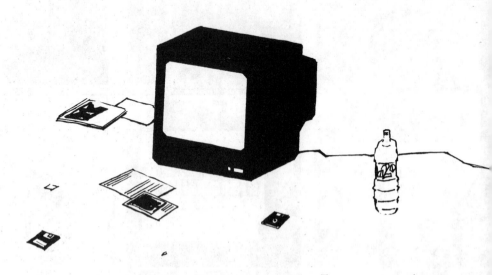

CONTINUED...

DISINFECT

is this you?
welcome to the future of america

PURGE

this is you.
welcome to the human race

I remember Jennie 2.5 from way back, during the protests.
Well, if you can call them protests.

I'm old enough to remember demonstrating against the Gulf Wars,
and the human rights violations in China. But these 'Free the Media'
protests were little more than over-enthusiastic college students
showing off, making noise, going through the actions.

Maybe they cared about protecting their
First Amendment Rights. Maybe, but I doubt it.
Most of them anyway. The ones that were really
concerned were the ones behind the scenes,
planting worms and trojan horse viruses
into computers and payphones, anything
to counteract and safeguard their lifestyle
from what would manifest itself as the Clean Act.

Except Jennie. She straddled both lines.
She was into it, the subversive shit,
the breaking and entering, hacking, the
minor terrorism that enabled her to
broadcast her pirate TV show.

But she was always out on the street, in the protests, yelling and shouting, taunting and spitting in the riot cops faces. And when the cops got their orders, and the clubs were raised and the tear gas canisters started flying, she never surrendered. They would haul her away, and she was still fighting and kicking. I think she liked having all the attention.

She must have. She always got it.

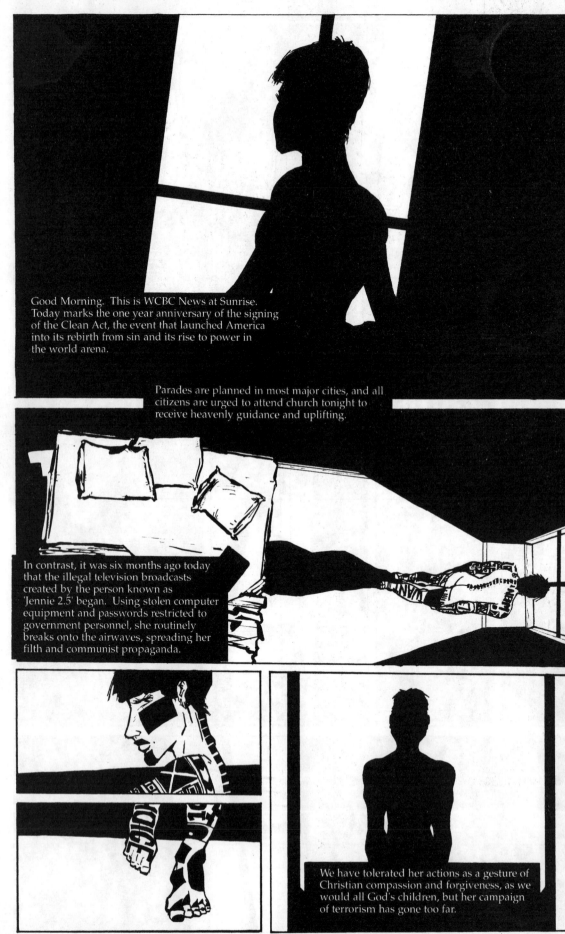

Good Morning. This is WCBC News at Sunrise.
Today marks the one year anniversary of the signing
of the Clean Act, the event that launched America
into its rebirth from sin and its rise to power in
the world arena.

Parades are planned in most major cities, and all
citizens are urged to attend church tonight to
receive heavenly guidance and uplifting.

In contrast, it was six months ago today
that the illegal television broadcasts
created by the person known as
'Jennie 2.5' began. Using stolen computer
equipment and passwords restricted to
government personnel, she routinely
breaks onto the airwaves, spreading her
filth and communist propaganda.

We have tolerated her actions as a gesture of
Christian compassion and forgiveness, as we
would all God's children, but her campaign
of terrorism has gone too far.

The global community is reeling this morning at reports of a massive crackdown on interne

This is not "art", citizens.

It is not harmless, and it is not legal.

We urge all our viewers to guard against being influenced by the broadcasts, and put your trust in your government to correct the problem.

MY MEN ARE READY TO MOVE *NOW*, SIR. AND I AM BEING AS PATIENT AS I CAN. FRANKLY, I CAN'T UNDERSTAND *WHY* YOU HAVE BEEN *HOLDING BACK* ALL THIS TIME.

and Boston describe riot police physically ripping out telephone lines and burning computer

NOT YET.

CONTROL.
CHECK.

across the American border in Canada have been broadcasting world news feeds over public

forces poised at the Texas/Mexico border. In response, the President ordered additional

I'M ALMOST DONE HERE.
I'VE OPENED UP THE BANDWIDTH ALL THE WAY,
AND THE TRANSMISSION COMPUTERS
WILL BE SENDING THIS OUT ON
EVERY FREQUENCY AVAILABLE.

LISTEN: ONCE THE TAPE STARTS ROLLING,
I NEED YOU TO COUNT TO TEN,
THEN LAUNCH THE KILLER INTO THE ROOT DIRECTORY.
IT WILL DISABLE THE VIRUS FIRST, AND ALLOW THE TAPE TO FINISH.
THEN IT WILL DESTROY ALL THE FILES THAT HAVE BEEN
MODIFIED IN THE LAST FIFTEEN MINUTES.
ONCE YOU LAUNCH THAT, PACK UP AND GET OUT OF THERE.

aircraft carriers into the Gulf of Mexico. Fleeing Apache tribes cornered in the Baja

THREE

The posting on Usenet said 730pm, WCBC,
right in the middle of Access Hollywood.
I was at home, the VCR set, ready and waiting.

Jennie's broadcasts had become a little predictable,
sometimes boring, and I really only watched because
there wasn't anything else I could deal with.

I had no idea she was going global
with that night's broadcast.
I mean, how could she possibly gain
access to that kind of equipment?
And the security must be insane.
They would be on top of her within minutes.

TWO

She would never get on the air.

ONE

"TRUST YOURSELVES ONLY! LOOK AND SEE WHAT'S GOING ON AROUND YOU! RESEARCH WHAT YOU DONT KNOW, DON'T LET OTHERS TELL YOU WHAT TO BELIEVE.

SIR?

IM JUST A TINY MAN

MUCHO MET

...

ANYTIME, SIR. WE ARE RIGHT ON TOP OF HER

TRUST YOUR TECHNOLUST

CAPTAIN, SHE IS YOURS.
PICK HER UP.

RIGHT!

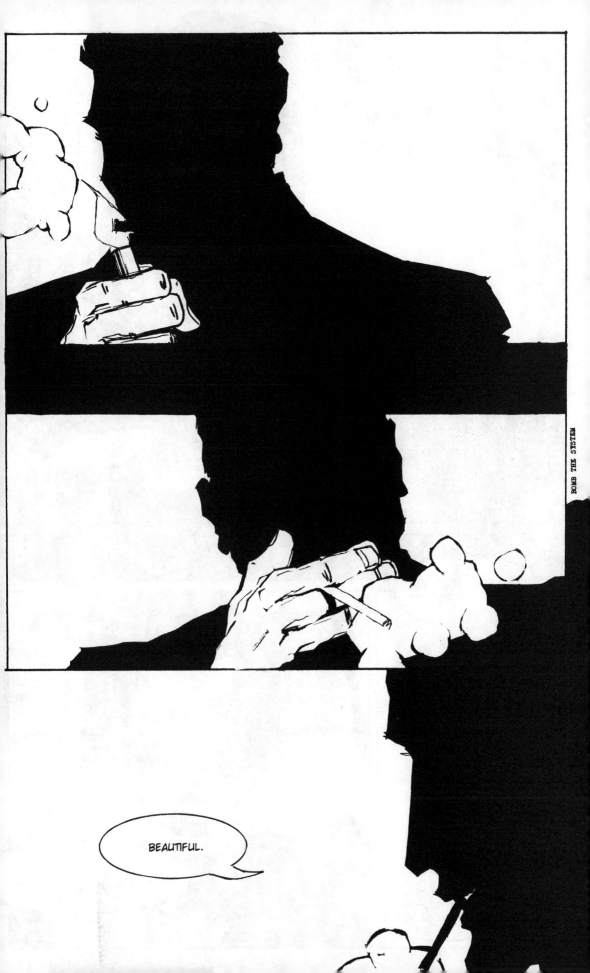

BACK AT THE HOUSE. WHAT *HAPPENED* TO YOU, ANYWAY? WE WERE ALL SURPRISED TO SEE YOU *RELEASED* SO *QUICKLY.*

DON'T BRING UP THE PAST. I'M HERE NOW, I WANT TO HELP, AND I CHECK OUT FINE. LET'S LEAVE IT AT THAT.

HEY, DON'T TAKE THAT THE WRONG WAY. I'M NOT *ACCUSING* YOU OF ANYTHING, ITS JUST THAT AMERICA ISN'T REALLY KNOWN FOR BEING *LENIENT* WITH ITS POLITICAL PRISONERS, *ESPECIALLY* ONE LIKE *YOU.*

C'MON, LETS GET GOING. I NEED TO MAKE A FEW CALLS AND CHECK MY MAIL.

THE AIR IS SO **CLEAN** HERE.

CAN I ASK YOU SOMETHING?

SURE.

WHY DID YOU COME HERE?

WHY AM I HELPING YOU, YOU MEAN? I DON'T KNOW GUESS I DON'T TAKE **DEFEAT** VERY WELL.

In the end, nothing really changed. TV was still the same,
so were the newspapers. The Clean Act was still firmly in
place, and Jennie 2.5 was dismissed as a fad. Some even thought
it was all a government fabrication designed to boost ratings and
to demonstrate the futility of resistance.

But she was real. She may not have had much of an effect on the
general population, but she did inspire a select few who made
efforts to follow in her footsteps. Rumor had it she had relocated
to Eastern Europe and was planning a comeback.

I knew Jennie 2.5 personally, and I knew she wouldnt give up.
This would prove to be only the first chapter in what would become
close to a decade of work spent fighting the Clean Act,
and its various reincarnations and copycats.

But for now, life went on as before.

And people seemed to like that just fine.

THE END.

MAKE
THEM
LISTEN.

CHANNEL >>ZERO

be heard!
photocopy this page.
use it wisely.

who do you love?

MAKE
THEM
UNDER
STAND.

CHANNEL >>ZERO

be heard!
photocopy this page.
use it everywhere.

who do you love?

"I wasn't wit' it, but just that very minute...
It occured to me
The suckers had authority."

- Chuck D

I SHOT THIS BASTARD BETWEEN THE EYES TODAY.

I DID IT BECAUSE IT WAS MY JOB AS A *CLEANER* AND MY *DUTY* AS A CITIZEN. THAT'S *CITIZEN* WITH A CAPITAL "C". LET'S NOT FORGET THE *BULLSHIT IMPORTANCE* PLACED UPON US BY THOSE WHO WOULD HAVE US TO THEIR BIDDING.

I WALKED HOME WITH THE BASTARD'S *BLOOD* ON MY CLOTHES AND HIS *FACE* ON MY MIND. IT WAS A LOOK OF PURE *SURPRISE* COMBINED WITH *SUSPICION*, AS THIS GUY WAS JUST MINUTES AGO *EYEBALLING* ME ON THE TRAIN. MAYBE HE THOUGHT I WAS FOLLOWING HIM BECAUSE I LIKED HIM.

IT'S ALL ABOUT A GOOD SALARY, GREAT BENEFITS, AND THE *WARM FEELING* YOU GET AT THE END OF THE DAY, WHEN YOU GO HOME TO YOUR SWEET APARTMENT; KNOWING THAT BECAUSE YOU *SHOT* A 14-YEAR-OLD FOR *KEY-SCRATCHING* THE J TRAIN, THAT WOULD SOME HOW IMPROVE THE *QUALITY OF LIFE* IN OUR CITY.

I'VE HEARD *ALL* THE ARGUMENTS. PROPERTY VALUES ARE UP, THE CRIME RATE IS DOWN TO WHAT IT WAS *THIRTY YEARS AGO,* THERE'S PLENTY OF PARKING, AND YOU CAN WALK THROUGH *TIMES SQUARE* WITHOUT HAVING TO DODGE *HOOKERS* AND *JUNKIES* AND *MUGGERS.*

JOIN THE COPS!

kick some ass!

AND GOOD LUCK TRYING TO BUY **PORN** IN MANHATTAN. YOU GOTTA TAKE **THREE TRAINS** TO SOME GOD-FORSAKEN **SHITHOLE** IN LONG ISLAND CITY. AND WHILE YOU'RE ON THE TRAIN, DON'T DROP YOUR GUM WRAPPER OR LEAVE YOUR **DAILY NEWS** ON THE SEAT 'CUZ I WILL APPEAR OUT OF **FUCKING NOWHERE** AND SHOOT YOU.

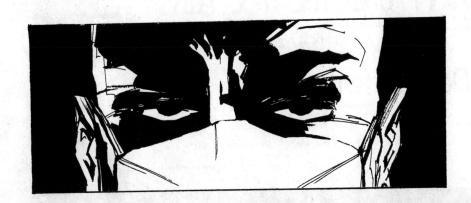

FREEDOM IS A VIRUS.

personal expression is a
small price to pay for peace and stability.

don't be part of the problem, be part of the future.

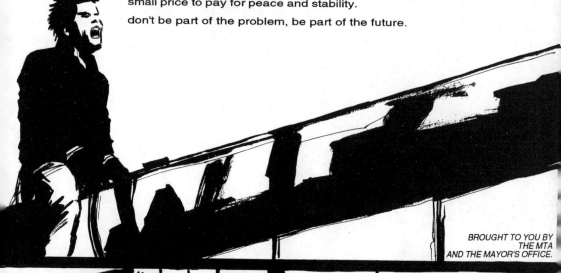

*BROUGHT TO YOU BY
THE MTA
AND THE MAYOR'S OFFICE.*

**ROCKING AND SHOCKING
THE STREETS AND TRAINS.**

**SLAMMING AND JAMMING
THE CRIMINAL**

The Team

**We have over 5,000
Guardian Angels.**

**Not only from coast to coast
also throughout Europe,
Australia and Canada.**

**A unique opportunity
to be judged by _what you do_.
Not by what race you are
or by what you say.**

**NYC Guardian Angels
█0█ WEST 4█ ST.
(OFF 8 AVE. MANH.)**

**YOU CAN RUN BUT
YOU CAN'T HIDE**

JOIN TODAY!

DARE TO CARE

DARE TO CARE

GUARDIAN
SAFETY PATROL
ANGELS

**IF YOU ARE
16 YEARS AND OLDER**
24hr
(212) █97-7█

DON'T BREATHE THE AIR!

Don't drink the water.
Don't walk in the park at night.
Don't trust your mayor.

Don't Listen!

the liberals are always sticking there noses where they
don't belong, looking for something, anything to complain
about. They see a "cause" around every corner.

don't be a victim to paranoia. we have things under control.
relax, live your lives.

the Mayor's Office

I'M FEARED BY MY FRIENDS AND FAMILY; *HATED* BY THE PEOPLE THAT MATTER THE MOST TO ME. MAYBE SOME RICH, OLD *WHITE WOMAN* FROM THE UPPER EAST SIDE LIKES ME BECAUSE WHEN SHE STEPS OUTSIDE, SHE ISN'T *FUCKIN' VISUALLY ASSAULTED* BY A NEWSPAPER BOX OR A HOTDOG VENDOR ON THE CORNER WHERE SHE DOESN'T THINK ONE SHOULD BE.

BUT THAT'S USELESS TO ME.

INSTEAD, WHAT HAPPENS EVERY NIGHT IS I GO HOME TO AN EMPTY APARTMENT WITH NO MESSAGES ON MY MACHINE, A FROZEN MICROWAVE DINNER, AND *300 CRAP CHANNELS* ON TV.

THERE ARE SOME PERKS. I CAN ALWAYS GET A CAB, AND I *NEVER* HAVE TO PAY. THE POOR DRIVER IS SO AFRAID I'LL REPORT HIM FOR SOME *BULLSHIT OFFENSE.* IF IT'S NOT *IMMIGRATION* HOUNDING THE POOR GUY, IT'S THE *MAYOR'S BRAND NEW FUCKING COURTESY CODE,* WHICH TELLS ME, THE PASSENGER, THAT I AM ENTITLED TO A VOYAGE OF SUCH *ASS-KISSING COMFORT* AND *SILKY-SMOOTH NAVIGATION* AND IF EVERY SINGLE ONE OF MY *WHIMS* IS NOT *CATERED TO,* THE COWERING DRIVER IS SUBJECT TO A VERITABLE *ONSLAUGHT* OF FINES AND TICKETS.

AND I DON'T HAVE TO LEAVE A TIP

A LOT OF PEOPLE CALL ME A COP. *CLEANERS* AREN'T POLICEMEN, NOT LIKE IT MAKES MUCH OF A DIFFERENCE. WE BOTH CARRY GUNS AND ARE OUT TO ENFORCE THE LAW. BUT I'M NOT A COP. COPS IN NEW YORK HAVE MORE IMPORTANT DUTIES TO ATTEND TO, LIKE *BEATING UP KIDS IN WASHINGTON HEIGHTS* OR *ACCEPTING BLOWJOBS* AS BRIBES FROM *HOOKERS* ALONG THE WESTSIDE HIGHWAY.

CLEANERS DEAL WITH A SPECIFIC ISSUE OF CITY CLEANLINESS, WHICH IS RELATED TO *PERSONAL* CLEANLINESS, WHICH IS, OF COURSE, TO SAY, *MORAL CLEANLINESS*. FUCK, I WORK FOR THE LAW, AND I'M STILL AT A LOSS TO EXPLAIN HOW *THAT* WORKS. I DON'T KNOW, THE CARDINAL IS *BLOWING THE MAYOR* WHO IS IN TURN *BLOWING THE ENTIRE CITY COUNCIL* WHO PASSES THESE *BULLSHIT* LAWS WITHOUT US KNOWING UNTIL ITS ALL OVER AND THEN ITS TOO LATE.

SOME PEOPLE ASK ME *WHY* I BECAME A CLEANER

THAT'S THE REAL QUESTION, ISN'T IT?

THE MOST *OBVIOUS* ANSWER IS SOMETHING LIKE "MY DAD WAS A CLEANER", OR "I WANT TO MAKE THE STREETS CLEAN FOR OUR CHILDREN", OR EVEN SOMETHING LIKE "MY PARENTS WERE KILLED BY RANDOM LITTERING, SO I'VE DEDICATED MY LIFE TO CLEANLINESS". FUCK *THAT* NOISE. THAT SORT OF SHIT IS FOR *STUPID PEOPLE* WHO DON'T KNOW ANY BETTER.

I JOINED THE *CLEANERS* FOR THE SIMPLE REASON THAT I WAS *BRAINWASHED*. I USED TO BE A REAL TV JUNKIE, PISSING AWAY MY LIFE WATCHING *MUST SEE FUCKING TEDIUM*, AND THE *SATURDAY MORNING PILE OF HORSESHIT*. SO WHEN CITY ELECTIONS STARTED BEING TELEVISED, I GOT HOOKED. MY BRAIN HAD BEEN *NUMBED* BY TALK SHOWS YEARS AGO, SO I WAS AN EASY TARGET. I LEARNED TO *TRUST* THE MAYOR, I *BELIEVED IN HIM*, I VOTED FOR HIM.

AND WHEN HE FORMED THE CLEANERS, I JOINED.

WE NOW ACCEPT

IT DIDN'T TAKE ME TOO LONG TO FIGURE OUT I HAD
FUCKED UP, BUT IT WAS TOO LATE. TOO MANY STRIK
TEAMSTERS AND CAB DRIVERS PROMPTED THE CITY TO
PASS LEGISLATURE REQUIRING **MANDATORY 6-YEAR**
TERMS OF EMPLOYMENT FOR MUNICIPAL EMPLOYEES

THE **PUNISHMENTS** FOR THOSE WITH THE **BALLS** TO **TRY AND QUIT**
WERE SEVERE, AND I WASN'T ABOUT TO GET DUMPED INTO THE **HUDSON**
IN A **ZIPLOCK** AT 5AM. I DID MY JOB AND MET MY QUOTAS AND KEPT
TRYING FOR EARLY REPRIEVE.

BACK TO THE *BASTARD*, THE ONE PUTTING UP *ILLEGAL POSTERS*, THE ONE LYING ON A *SLAB* IN THE CITY MORGUE WITH A *BULLET HOLE* IN HIS HEAD, THE *FUCKING COCKSUCKER* THAT FORCED ME TO MAKE MYSELF A *MURDERER* FOR THE *HUNDREDTH TIME.*

I FEEL PRETTY *SHITTY* ABOUT KILLING HIM, BUT THAT'LL ONLY LAST A COUPLE DAYS. WHAT REALLY BOTHERS ME IS THAT I *AGREED* WITH WHAT HE WAS DOING.

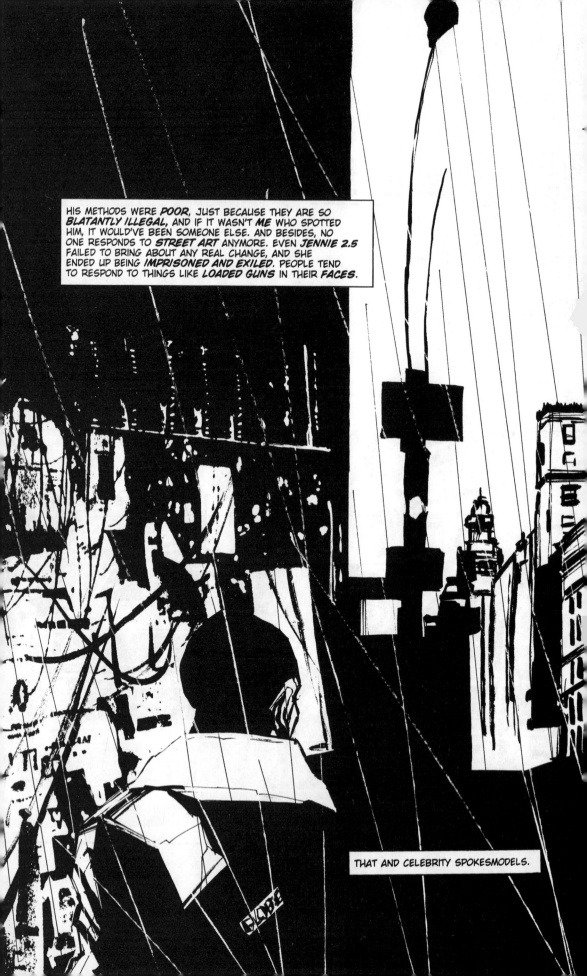

HIS METHODS WERE *POOR*, JUST BECAUSE THEY ARE SO *BLATANTLY ILLEGAL*, AND IF IT WASN'T *ME* WHO SPOTTED HIM, IT WOULD'VE BEEN SOMEONE ELSE. AND BESIDES, NO ONE RESPONDS TO *STREET ART* ANYMORE. EVEN *JENNIE 2.5* FAILED TO BRING ABOUT ANY REAL CHANGE, AND SHE ENDED UP BEING *IMPRISONED AND EXILED*. PEOPLE TEND TO RESPOND TO THINGS LIKE *LOADED GUNS* IN THEIR *FACES*.

THAT AND CELEBRITY SPOKESMODELS.

HIS IDEOLOGY WAS SOUND. HE HAD A *CLARITY* AND AN *UNDERSTANDING* OF THE SITUATION THAT MOST OF US *DON'T* HAVE. HE KNEW THAT THE CURRENT SYSTEM IS *SHIT* AND *DIRECT ACTION* IS NEEDED. SITTING IN FRONT OF THE TV DOESN'T HELP. GOING OUT AND RISKING YOUR LIFE TO GET THE MESSAGE SPREAD IS *BETTER*, BUT ULTIMATELY RATHER POINTLESS, CONSIDERING HE'S *DEAD*. THAT'S WHY THE MORE I THINK ABOUT IT, THE MORE I REALIZE THAT MAYBE IT'S NOT UP TO THE AVERAGE CITIZEN TO START THE REVOLUTION.

MAYBE IT'S UP TO PEOPLE WITH *POWER*.
MAYBE IT'S UP TO THE *CLEANERS*.

MAYBE ITS UP TO ME.

THE CITY **HAS** TO **CHANGE.** THE MAYOR'S **REIGN OF TERROR** NEEDS TO END, AND THE ONLY WAY I SEE IT HAPPENING IS A **FUCKING** BLOODY **COUP.**

WE NEED TO STORM **CITY HALL** AND CLEAN IT OUT. GRACIE MANSION NEEDS TO **BURN.** THE PEOPLE THAT AREN'T **DOWN WITH THE PROGRAM** SHOULD BE HAULED OUT INTO THE STREET AND **BEATEN** INTO SUBMISSION. I SEE IT AS A **MAD** RIOTING SCENE, WITH THE **CLEANERS** AND THE **JENNIE UNDERGROUND** LEADING THE WAY - YOU EITHER JOIN US OR **DIE.**

PUT THE *MOTHERFUCKING BOOT IN.*

I COULD MAKE A HALF DOZEN PHONE CALLS AND GET THIS STARTED.
AS SOON AS WE GOT SHIT *ROLLING*, THE COPS WOULD FALL INTO LINE,
SINCE THE *LAST THING* THEY WANT TO DO IS END UP ON THE *LOSING
SIDE*. MOST OF THE PEOPLE WOULD ACCEPT THE CHANGE EASILY, AND THE
FEW THAT RESIST WOULD BE NO MATCH.

TEN THOUSAND ANGRY AND ARMED *MOTHERFUCKERS* WITH
RUDY'S BLOODY DECAPITATED HEAD ON A *STICK* MARCHING
UP BROADWAY. WHO WOULD STOP US?

global supermarket

"When one voice rules the nation
just because they're top of the pile
doesn't mean their vision is the clearest."

-Billy Bragg

Moustafa McGowan: 17, born and raised in Egypt.
Moved with family to New York eight years ago.
Attends Stuyvesant. Spends summers working as
a courier. Knows the NYC streets very well. Drinks
ice coffee. A speed freak. Indulges in petty theft,
usually credit cards, phonecard numbers, ATM pin codes.
Expert "shoulder-surfer". Caught last year by a Cleaner,
was arrested, detained for a week, beaten hourly and
denied food. Family lost its lawsuit against the City.
Moustafa joined the Resistance the day he was
discharged from the hospital. He has a girlfriend:

Special: 17, classmate and girlfriend of Moustafa.
Native New Yorker, father is a local politician and a
member of the American Aryan Militia. She carries
a gun and bottle of Poland Spring everywhere she goes.
Expert speaker and writer. Produces zines (illegal),
and distributes them amongst her friends in the
Resistance. People tend to fear her because of her
father, her gun, her knowledge, and her resemblance
to Jennie 2.5.

Special and Moustafa, May 1997

A little over a year ago, the world met Jennie 2.5. Out of the American media void came a little voice, thundering amidst the silence.

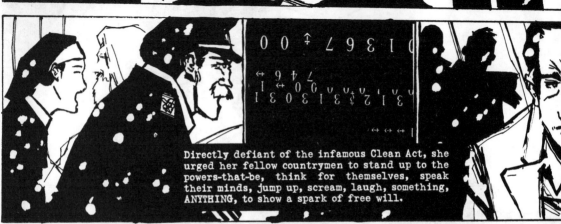

Directly defiant of the infamous Clean Act, she urged her fellow countrymen to stand up to the powers-that-be, think for themselves, speak their minds, jump up, scream, laugh, something, ANYTHING, to show a spark of free will.

She beamed this message over the air-waves, a pirate television broadcast, into every home in America.

rejected

The American Propaganda Works had done an excellent job of numbing the brains of its citizens, and Jennie's pleas fell on apathetic ears. She was a curiosity, a television programme people assumed was intentional, and paid it no mind.

It wasn't until she was chased and arrested on live TV that people perked up, and finally paid attention.

my main objective is to be more effective

Her trial was televised, as an example to the people of what happens if you defy the established order. She was imprisoned for a short time, then exiled. Within America, and the rest of the world, the myth of Jennie 2.5 is well known, and many imitators have sprung up in her absence. None have come close to achieving what she has.

Out of the public eye for several months, she reappears and talks with Bad Floppies about her exile, her possible return to public life and to America, and also to address the rumours that have spread: her ties to China and to Castro, her militant political beliefs, and her plans for the future.

defamation innue
speed dial
BadFLOPPIES UK: Jennie 2.5, you are in political exile, without a country to call home. Do you miss it? America, New York?

recommended daily allowance

JENNIE 2.5: It's not quite as simple as that. I mean, yeah, I love New York, I miss the skyline, the people, the food, all that stuff. What I DON'T miss is what America is now. It's terrifying. It's terrifying just from what I hear from abroad, and that's only what they choose to tell us. I caught the President's speech on WorldCast a few days ago, and he used the term National Socialism to describe his administration... everyone knows that's a fancy way of saying Nazi.

inoculate

fully customizable

BADF: The President is a Nazi?

J25: You tell me.

BADF: I would certainly consider some of his practices suspicious, but Nazi is a pretty harsh word.

J25: He said it, not me.

🚇 Subway

twentyfour hour relief

BADF: True. You've made your intentions to break your exile and return to America public knowledge. And it seems these intentions to spread the word will guarantee American authorities to be waiting for you when you arrive. Why are you taking this risk, and aren't you worried about your safety?

6→636⌠756↝6©000080000001000616↝697311↝↝70027⌠04551⌡14↝⌠212001⌠⌠2⌠32↝65011⌡000↝2

4 1 5 3 2 0 3 1 2⌠3 1 3 0 3 1 2⌠3 1 3 0 0⌠0 0 0 0 0 0 0 4 0 ↦ ↦ ↦ ↦ ↦ ↦ ↦ ↦ ↦ ↦ ↦ ↦ ↦ 0 0 0 1 0 0 0 2 0 1 ↦

⌢⌢⌠3⌢1 3 0 3 1 2⌢⌠3 1 3 0 0⌢⌠0 0 0 0 0 0 4
0 7 0 ↦ 1 0 0 0 0 2 0 0 0⌠3 ↦ ↦ ↦ ↦ ⌠0 0
7 4 6 ↦ 6 1 7 0 7 0 6⌠7 5 6⌢↝©↦⌡00

6 7 ⌡ 0 0 0 2 0 0 1

J25: Yes, and no. I don't expect to be immediately arrested. I do expect to be trailed and bugged. They exiled me instead of imprisoning me for a reason. I probably should have been killed. I think its because I am well known, and I have the ability to generate interest in whatever, and they like that. I think they want me to work for them.

↦↦500040↝↝6377696⌠0↝↝↦↦400182⌠636↦7265636⌠7465↦
6⌡6973636⌡7669736⌠756©6©↦↦↦↦8000000010006↦626↦
↦↝⌠↝001630000969636↦6⌠7372656374000969636↦6⌠735↦

6 ↝ 0 1 0 0 0 4 6 ↝ 0 1 0
↝⌡7 2©⌠8©1 2↦6↝0©00094↦
3 2©⌠⌡2©4 5 5 1 6 0 0 0 1 0 4↦5↦
6 1 0 0 1 1 6⌡2↦1⌠2 5 5↦0 0 1 0 6 1

frolic

6

BADF: I assume you won't.

6973636 7669736 756 6 8000000010006 626 200 00040 706973660 00182 6 697363616374766 756
001630000969636 6 737265637400096963 6 735265637 0 900040 70696 730 8001230000777696 726563
6 0 1 0 0 0 4 6 0 1 0 9 0 0 0 2 36 2 5 2 0
72 8 12 6 0 00094 2 2 65011 000 2 6 0 0
32 2 45516000104 5 00106100116 2 61001 16 2
6100116 2 1 255 00106100116 2 6100116100122 1

J25: Nope. I have reasons for going back,
but that is certainly not one of them.

30312 31300 000000040

BADF: What are they? Do they have anything to do
with the rumours you've been recently sighted in
Beijing and several Latin American countries?

J25: You know about that?

BADF: You're an important cultural icon. It's my responsibility to know these things.

J25: Christ, word gets around. I should get these removed (points at facial tattoos).

BADF: Seriously?

J25: I don't know. I've had a few taken off, but I think I need them. Instant recognizability holds a lot of power. Is that a word? Recognizability? (laughs)

LOCKER 129, BABE. THERE'S SOME CASH AND CARD NUMBERS.

LEAVE BY THE LOWER LEVEL - GOES STRAIGHT INTO THE SUBWAY.

SEE YOU LATER, RIGHT? BROOKLYN AT...

TWO.

..AT TWO. COOL?

your worst enemy.

your ultimate salvation.

MADONNA
AND
CHILD

who do you love?

Sue Sze: 19, student at the Cuban Military Intelligence Academy. Member of the Daughters Of Che, a sanctioned pro-revolution group designed to promote the ideal of Armed Struggle in Latin America. A web freak and top notch research expert. Introduced to Jennie 2.5 four months ago during a tour of the Academy. Exchanged email and cell phone numbers.

Sue, May Day, 1995

BADF: Well then? The China and Latin America visits?

J25: My notoriety has earned me lots of friends around the world, and I spent a couple months traveling, privileged to be the guest of many nations, not just China and Cuba. Actually, it's quite startling. Americans really have NO idea what is happening in the rest of the world.

BADF: Care to elaborate?

havana...

THE M VIRUS

J25: Well, the media blackout really does an excellent job. The world is passing America by. If and when they finally open their eyes, they will be confronted by a very different world than they remember.

BADF: You mean recent events, like Russia and India joining NATO.

more propaganda

J25: Exactly. The government's scared shitless with this information. But they withhold it, away from the people. The people don't know anything.

BADF: Yet your opinions, being so radical and extreme, are favored by the masses. Then where does that leave you, in support or by yourself?

J25: That leaves me as a political enemy of the state, returning home. Exactly when and how, I can't say, and what I will do when I get there, I can't say that either. But just like before, I can't just sit back and not do anything.

hate au lait

TIENES EL APOYO COMPLETO DE LAS HIJAS DE CHE.

>> You have the full support of the Daughters Of Che.

BADF: You could hardly operate within America again, rig...

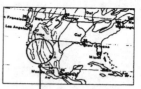

estimated area of conflict.
US warplanes prevent aerial
reconnaissance.

two sisters, aged 7 and 16, pose with weapons recently
supplied by the L.A.C.A.S.

this poorly digitized photo, recently sent out via email
from our news correspondent in Mexico shows a peasant
population preparing themselves for a war with America
they will, in all likelihood, lose. and with their defeat will
come death, starvation, slave labor, and conscription into
the mighty American war machine. this is Imperialism at its worst.

who watches who?   who watches you?

why?

bad floppies OK
who do you love?

the exact reason for America's sudden and violent
trespasses into Mexico are unknown, but intercepted
government documents point to racial bias and
religious zeal as a major motive. one cannot rule out
greed as a factor, however, considering the role it has
played in past American military ventures.

its only logical to assume that once Mexico falls,
its Central American neighbours will be next.

Heavy: 28, student at Vancouver Film School. Originally from Seattle, he smuggles information and supplies across the border to friends and family on a regular basis. Formed a Resistance chapter in Canada two months ago to support the anti-American struggle.

Tadpole and Heavy, 1992

Tadpole: 22, student at Emily Carr. Longtime friend of Heavy, helps out with his information trafficking and maintains a website and database for the Resistance internationally. Bought a copy of the Anarchist Cookbook a year ago and runs a small bomb factory from her basement.

J25: They couldn't. I epitomize The One Who Fought Them and Won, more or less. I am Hope, and the last thing America wants its people feeling is hope. They would kill me before that happened, for sure. I want to see my home, see my friends, and get a feel for the political climate. After that, we shall see.

welcome to the land

BADF: Would you consider you've made some effective contribution to the world by spreading your message?

J25: I think I managed to get everyone's attention quite well. What I do from this point on will determine if I have made an effective contribution.

BADF: Since you've been exiled have you worked on any projects abroad?

J25: Nothing like what I've done before. I've spoken at a few universities, some public works projects in developing areas. I've spent most of my time compiling contacts and resources. I have a long road ahead of me.

BADF: Another rumor: you're not an American citizen anymore.

J25: I'm not.

BADF: What nationality are you?

J25: America stripped me of my citizenship when I was exiled. I'm officially a World Citizen. Officially.

burn with them

BADF: How about unofficially? What about all the nations you have been visiting recently?

J25: I have a lot of friendly countries on my side, but I need my World Passport for now.

BADF: Were you ashamed to be American?

J25: Sometimes, yes. If you could see the kids dying of starvation in the streets of Baghdad, you would be ashamed too.

BADF: I see. On a lighter note, what do you think of the t-shirts?

reel

J25: I'm flattered. I went out clubbing in London last night, and they were everywhere. It used to be Hello Kitty and Anime when I was in back in New York, now its Jennie 2.5. I bought a few as souvenirs.

BADF: Were you recognized?

J25: Sort of. I think they assumed I was a wannabe with paint on her face. But I was in Berlin recently and was recognized in a club. It was a little frightening.

BADF: How so?

J25: I was just stared at. One kid touched my arm. That's it. It was eerie in its awkwardness. Neither of us knew what to do, how to react. I ended up leaving.

BADF: Weird.

J25: It was. People were much cooler in China. They would ask me stuff: real questions, smart questions. If it was America, they would just demand autographs and run off.

BADF: Superficial, but they are still, in fact, supporting your cause.

quality of life

J25: They seem to be supporting their own little cause. I wonder how much they can sell my autograph for?

BADF: Is that what happens?

J25: From what I hear.

BADF: Wow. What about other places you've visited? You mentioned Cuba.

J25: I did?

BADF: Yeah.

J25: Oh. Well, Cuba was a cool place. I have a lot of respect for Castro and his administration. I mean, they stood up to America, said 'fuck you', and got away with it. Even with the Soviets backing them, it's still pretty hardcore. And they WON.

BADF: You're compared to Che a lot.

J25: I heard that a couple times. I don't agree. He is a revolutionary god. Committed, tough, self-sacrificing. He changed the world. I wish I could be that way.

BADF: In many ways you are.

J25: No I'm not. I could be, maybe. I want to be.

BADF: Is that what you have planned? Armed struggle? A revolution?

J25: America would certainly benefit from a revolution. A lot of similarities can be drawn from its current state to Batista's Cuba in 1958. In that case, a dozen determined men with virtually no resources overthrew the government, thumbed their noses at the world, and are still in power 40 years later. If they did it, someone could do it with America.

BADF: Someone like you?

J25: Someone like me.

BADF: Specifically you?

J25: I can't answer that.

BADF: Are you a Communist?

J25: I've been called that. I've been called a Socialist, a Leninist-Marxist, an Anarchist. Call me all of those if you want. I am what you see before you.

BADF: You wrote an article for the Review recently, in which praised Maoist theory.

J25: Mao probably had the clearest vision of them all. He was a genius. It's no wonder China is as powerful as it is.

BADF: What about Tibet? And its blatant human rights violations?

J25: American exaggerations. I mean, those things exist. What China did to Tibet is unspeakable, I offer no excuses for them. But its not always as simple as we make it out to be. One common Western trait to assume your views are correct and everyone else's is wrong.

Who are we, as Westerners, to say that China can't stomp all over Tibet if they want to? It's their business. We aren't the police of the world, despite what America says or does. We don't have to like it, but forcing our opinions on everyone is wrong.

BADF: Point taken. But it's a chilling stance to take. It's not a popular stance.

J25: I know its not. But it's the CORRECT opinion.

ONE OF THE STEWARDESSES. SHE'S BLOND, ABOUT 35-40. SHE'LL HAND YOU A PASSPORT AND VISA. MEET US OUT FRONT. WE CAN TALK ABOUT THE BORDER THEN.

BADF: Good luck convincing people of that.

human medical experimentation--

it's like a bad dream.

but it happened. the japanese. the nazis.

a horrible by-product of conflict. prisoners of war put to use.

countries looking for an advantage. any advantage

but that was a long time ago. we are more civilized now.

Nevada. 1998.
a small government-funded research complex.

a paranoid America. millennial dread. world opinion not in their favor.

they turn to history for answers.

--it never went away.

who do you love?

Jennie 2.5: exiled American, revolutionary, leader of the anti-American resistance. Media slut, info-fetishist, political terrorist. Brought to worldwide attention through her pirate television broadcasts, and the cult followers falling in behind her. Mid-twenties, ex-New Yorker, exact whereabouts unknown.

J25: Well, I plan to be in America by the time this interview hits the stands. I still have the problem of getting past customs, and getting the needed cards and IDs to get by once I am there. I have some people on that as we speak.

BADF: You are going to just fly into JFK?

J25: I didn't say that. I mean, it may be that simple, or not. There are groups in Canada and Mexico that would be happy to help me out, but the border guards in America are pretty severe, so maybe I will have to think a little unconventionally. Any ideas?

BADF: Umm...

J25: I'm kidding. I'm not worried. I'll make it in. Getting out may be a different story.

BADF: Good luck with that. Do you consider yourself to be a role model?

J25: You mean like for kids?

BADF: Whomever.

probable cause

label

onSITE TV

J25: Jesus, I don't know. If I say yes, I open myself up for all sorts of shit. I mean, I think what I do is right, but would I suggest it to a 12-year-old? Maybe. Probably not. It's good not having to be responsible for anyone but yourself. That's why I never took on partners, aside from my street contacts.

But when I see teenage girls with Jennie 2.5 shirts on, it feels good. I would like to know that my efforts aren't in vain, that I maybe inspired the next generation of little revolutionaries.

BADF: We should wrap this up. Anything you want to add?

J25: Can I ask you something?

BADF: Sure.

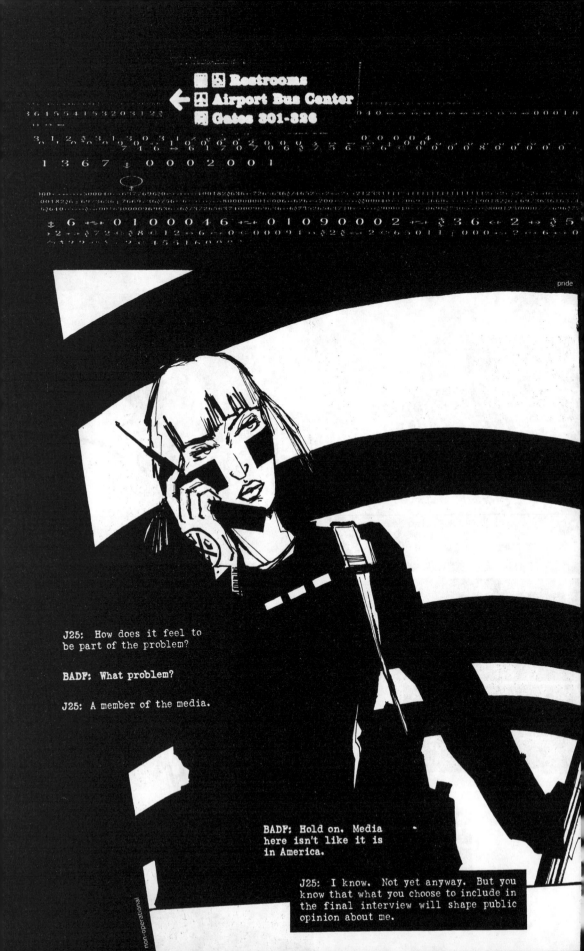

BADF: Yes, that's what media does...

J25: That's what writers do, what producers so. "Media" is a tool you use. It doesn't have a mind of its own. What sort of article does your editor want this to be?

BADF: I'm not sure I know what you mean...

J25: What's the hidden agenda? All media sources have one.

I'M ABOUT TO BOARD. THANKS FOR ALL YOUR HELP. SEE YOU SOON.

BADF: My agenda is my pay-check, and advancement in this field. I'll write a great article, for that reason.

J25: You have a considerable amount of power here, over me. I hope you use it well.

hands free

new and improved

i'm the perfect host

subversion perversion

After the interview, she took a short tour of our offices and left. Her cell phone had rung several times during our discussion, and she excused herself each time to answer it. She checked her email before she left. She turned down our offers for dinner.

19

She carries herself with a sort of pride, a determination, and a little bit of ego. I was left wondering what its like to wander the globe without a place to call home, being pulled in several directions by countries and corporations that all want her for themselves.

She is very much aware of her importance and her role in world events, whatever may happen.

I am left with a feeling of excited unpredictability. Whatever she does, wherever, whenever, its gonna be fucking huge. I can't wait.

DRTY DATA

"I'LL BE GENTLE"

>.as
global citizens entering
the third millenium, free
and un*restrict*ed communi-
cation with each other is
essential and inevitable.
state borders
will cease to exist, race
will become a non-issue,
and social--

standing and caste
status will be obliterat-
ed.   digital existence is
the next step in human
development.   the
cerulean hue of
active-matrix samsung
laptop flatscreens will
reflect in the eyes of our
children who sit in
libraries jacked into a
T3, fingers tapping notes
to penpals half a planet
away at
several hundred kilo-
bytes
a second.
the
collective keystrokes of
a world's population will
define who we are, as a
species of animals at

mental lightspeed.